A RUNAWAY SUCCESS

Contents

Adapted by Benjamin Hulme-Cross

A RUNAWAY SUCCESS

Thanks, Mr Bradawl! Bye, Dibber!
He's strange, Mr Bradawl. What would he need six pond nets for?

Mr Wallace is a brilliant inventor. He often comes here to buy things for his latest project.
What is his latest project?

I ... I don't know. I've never asked him!

Later
Time to close the shop, Dibber.
Yes, Mr Bradawl.

You've got me thinking, you know. I wonder what Mr Wallace is making.
CLOSED

Being an inventor must be fun. Better than being stuck in this shop!

It must feel so good to make something that really works!
CLOSED

CLOSED

ANTI-PESTO
PIGEON
CATCHER

Two days later

Morning, Mr Wallace! How can I help you today?
Just a few things, Mr Bradawl. A locking piston, two propellers and a fire extinguisher.

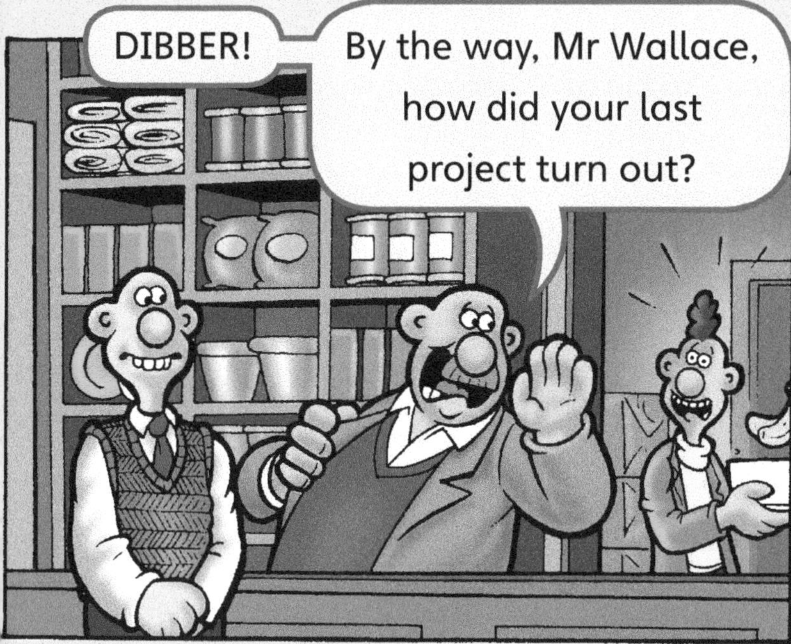
DIBBER!
By the way, Mr Wallace, how did your last project turn out?

Oh, that. Well, you might say it was a *runaway* success.
Excellent! I thought so.

Anything else on your list?
Well, I need some canoe paddles and some rubber sheeting to make a balloon with.

Coming right up!

Later, Mr Bradawl and Dibber are on another job

Paddles and a balloon! I wish I could see what Mr Wallace is making.

Me too!

JOE'S CAFE
EST 1896
JOE'S CAFE
BANANAS
APPLES
It's probably another runaway success!
The end

THE AMAZING BRASS BAND MACHINE

It's breakfast time for Wallace and Gromit. But it sounds as if someone is choking ...
Eh? What's this? Cough! Cough!
WEST WALLABY STREET

Cough! Cough! No more brass band?
Cough! Cough! Help, Gromit!
THE DAILY BUGLE

Phew! Thanks for that, Gromit.
This news about the brass band was such a shock, my toast went down backwards.

Look!
HE DAILY BUGLE
OCAL BRASS BAND
O DISBAND!

That band is part of this town! Sundays in the park won't be the same without the band playing. But don't worry, Gromit ...
THE DAILY BUGLE

We're going to save the band!

That Sunday they go to the park
Oh dear! There aren't many people watching the band.
No wonder! Their music's more painful than my back!
Hello! I'm told you're going to stop playing.
That's right. This is the last time.
Nobody wants
listen any more

But you *can't* give it up!
Well, we're not very good, and we just don't like being a band any more.

But there's always been a band here! This band is part of this town!

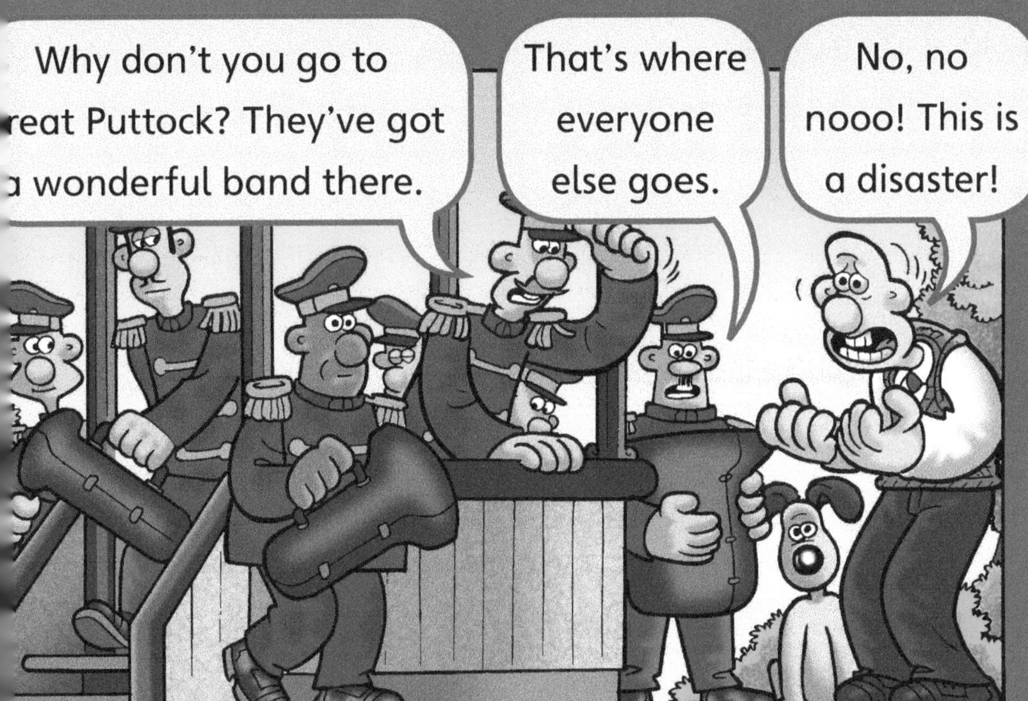
Why don't you go to
reat Puttock? They've got
a wonderful band there.
That's where everyone else goes.
No, no nooo! This is a disaster!

Hang on, I've got an idea!

you aren't using them any more, can I have your instruments?
I don't see why not.

Later, back at home, Wallace is in his shed ...

Oh, hello, Gromit. You'll never guess what I'm making. Could I have a cup of tea? I think we'll be here all night.

Oh, and you'd bett
bring a shovel as
well. And a clothe
peg for my nose ...

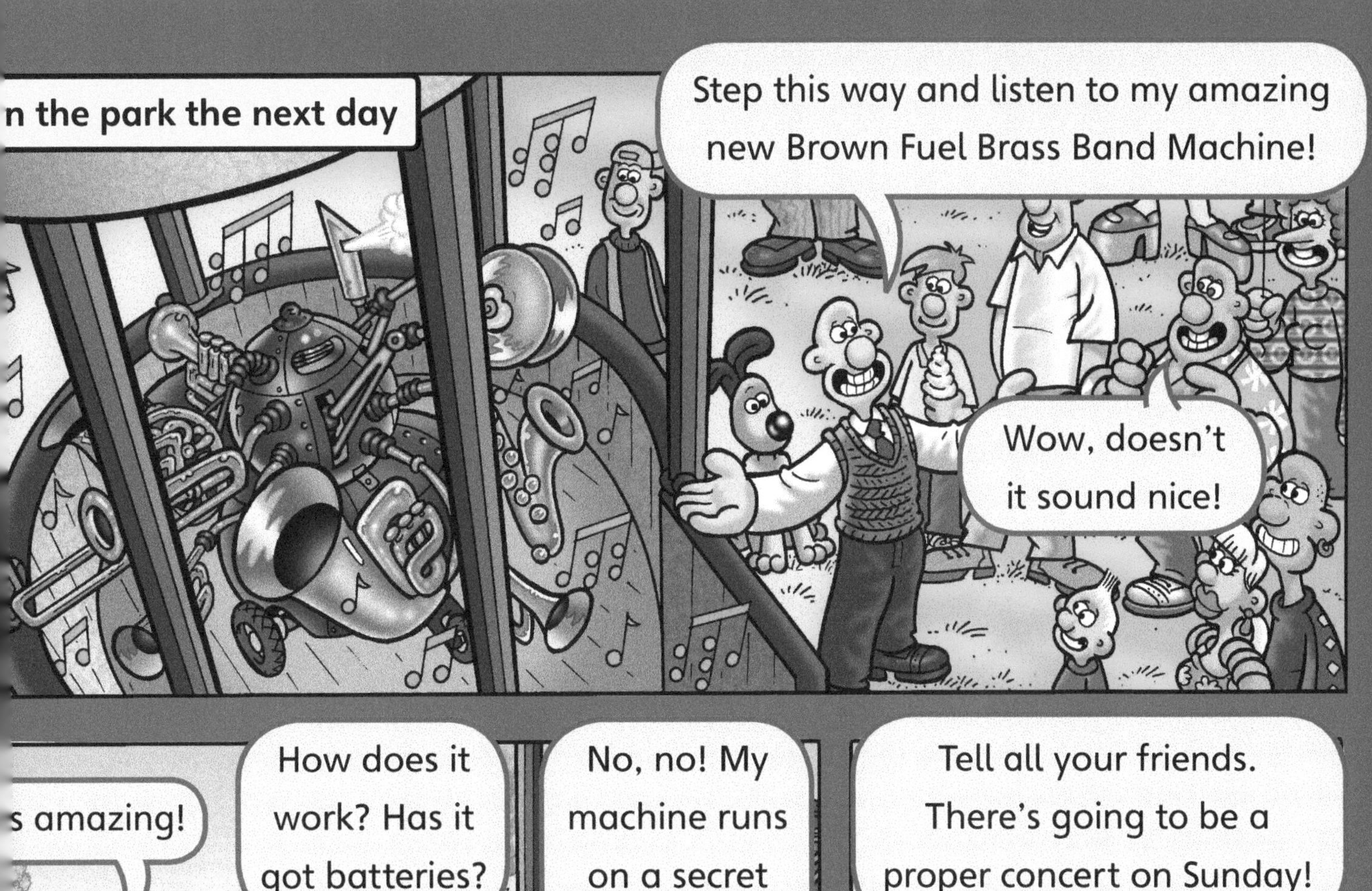
n the park the next day
Step this way and listen to my amazing new Brown Fuel Brass Band Machine!
Wow, doesn't it sound nice!

s amazing!
How does it work? Has it got batteries?
No, no! My machine runs on a secret type of fuel.

Tell all your friends. There's going to be a proper concert on Sunday!
This Sunday! Come and hear the amazing new Brown Fuel Brass Band Machine!

nat night, in nearby
reat Puttock
What? Have you seen this?

"Amazing new Brown Fuel Brass Band Machine ..."
No machine can be as good as a real band!
Stupid idea!

Stupid or not, people will want to see that machine – instead of listening to us! We need to put a stop to this.
Yeah!
He's right!

Let's go to the park this Sunday and sho that machine what we think of it!

That Sunday

Oh Gromit, so many people are here to listen to my machine!
Look, that lady in the hat is the mayor!

I'll go and say hello. Gromit, you stay here and give the machine plenty of our secret fuel.

We have to stop that machine!
Yeah!

We're the Great Puttoc band. No machine is better than us! Come o let's break it!

What a super machine!
Thank you, Mayor!
I hear it's even good for the environment!

Well yes, the secret fuel is certainly ... natural.

This way!

Let's have a look.
Is it me, or can I smell manure?
It's you.

Hey! Keep that dog away from me!
Sit! *S–it!*

He's not sitting!
Hold him back!

Now, if I turn this up, I bet the machine will break.

Er ... that doesn't look good.
Run for it!

I'm so glad you like my invention.
What *is* that dreadful noise?

Eh?

Oh no! Oh dear me no! Gromit? *Gromit?*

Oh dear, I may have turned it up too much.

Yuck!
Don't worry everyone. It's just our secret brown fuel.
You used manure for fuel?
I'm sorry, Mayor, we didn't mean to create such a stink!
It's the Great Puttock Brass Band! I'm your biggest fan Would you come and play i our park too? I'll pay you
Pay them
Oh well, Gromit. That's the end of this machine. It seems a shame to waste it, though.
Hang *on*, I've had an idea!
Later that summer
I'm so proud that we've won fir prize for the flowers in our park
We couldn't have done it without our amazing manure machine!
Well, there we are, Gromit. Now we've got a real brass band in the park, and our machine is helping the town too. You know what they say, Gromit … where there's brass, there's muck!
The e